The Ant and the Grasshopper

retold by Melissa Rothman
illustrated by John Wallner

One warm day, Grasshopper was in the grass.

He began to sing. Everyone heard his merry singing.

Before long, Ant came by.
Ant heard the singing, too.

Ant had some corn.
Ant was very little.
The corn was very big,
but it didn't fall.

Grasshopper glared at Ant.

"What are you doing?"
he asked.

Ant said, "I'm saving corn.
Someday I'll need to have it."

"But there is so much to eat," said Grasshopper. "Just look!"

"There is so much to eat now," Ant told Grasshopper. "But when it is cold, you will see what will happen."

"I can't think about that
now," Grasshopper told Ant.
"I'll see what will happen
when it gets cold."

Every day, Ant worked in haste. She saved a lot of corn.

Soon snow began to fall.

Grasshopper looked for something to eat. But he did not see a thing.

Grasshopper went to see Ant.

Ant gave Grasshopper something to eat.

"Next time, I will put away something before the cold comes," Grasshopper said.

"That will be good," Ant
said. "Now have a little
more to eat."

Comprehension Check

Retell the Story

Use a Beginning, Middle, and End Chart to retell the story.

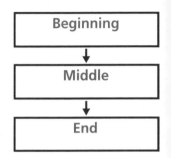

Think and Compare

1. At the end of the story, what did Grasshopper learn?

2. How are you a good friend?

3. Why is it important for people to save for another day?